ROSLEY
Stupid SCHOOL Trousers

Dramatised from
Susan Gates' story
by David Calcutt

Illustrated by Martin Remphrey

Oxford University Press

Oxford University Press, Great Clarendon Street, Oxford OX2 6DP

Oxford New York
Auckland Cape Town Dar es Salaam Hong Kong Karachi
Kuala Lumpur Madrid Melbourne Mexico City Nairobi
New Delhi Shanghai Taipei Toronto
With offices in
Argentina Austria Brazil Chile Czech Republic France Greece
Guatemala Hungary Italy Japan Poland Portugal Singapore
South Korea Switzerland Thailand Turkey Ukraine Vietnam

Oxford is a trade mark of Oxford University Press

First published 1998
10 9 8 7 6 5 4 3

Adapted from the novel **Stupid Trousers** by Susan Gates,
published by Oxford University Press in 1998.

ISBN-13: 978-0-19-918782-9
ISBN-10: 0-19-918782-7

Designed by Holbrook Design (Oxford) Limited

Printed in China

Cast list

Ross

Lee

1st Narrator

2nd Narrator

Kerry

Mum

Note: on stage throughout Scenes 1–4 is a chair, on which the trousers are placed.

Scene 1

The living room in Ross and Lee's home. **Ross** *enters, looking very angry. His elder brother,* **Lee***, follows him.* **Ross** *shouts out as he enters.*

Ross No! No way!

Lee Go on, Ross. Try them on.

Ross No, I said. No way!

Ross *turns his back on Lee and folds his arms. They both stand still, as the two* **narrators** *enter. The* **2nd Narrator** *carries a pair of red trousers, folded up. The* **narrators** *speak to the audience.*

1st Narrator *(Pointing at Ross)* That's Ross.

2nd Narrator *(Pointing at Lee)* And that's his big brother, Lee.

Lee *speaks to Ross.*

Lee	Just try them, Ross.
	Ross keeps his back turned towards Lee.
Ross	Didn't you hear me? I said no! No way!
	They stand still again as the two narrators speak.
1st Narrator	Ross is going to be a page boy at his big sister's wedding.
2nd Narrator	The wedding's tomorrow.
1st Narrator	And Ross has just seen the clothes he's got to wear.
2nd Narrator	A frilly shirt.
Ross	I hate that frilly shirt!
2nd Narrator	A red bow tie.
Ross	The bow tie's horrible!

1st Narrator	And a pair of red velvet trousers.
	*The **2nd Narrator** holds up the trousers.*
2nd Narrator	Which he really doesn't like at all.
	*The **2nd Narrator** puts the trousers on a chair.*
Ross	I hate those stupid trousers!
Lee	Why?

Ross	They're too long!

> **Ross** *picks up the trousers and holds them up.*

Ross	Look at them! They'll trip me up! Everyone will laugh at me!
Lee	No, they won't.
Ross	Yes, they will! And you can shut up! Those trousers are stupid, and you're stupid as well!
Lee	I'm not stupid! You are!

> **Kerry** *enters.*

Kerry	Don't say that to your brother, Lee.
1st Narrator	That's Kerry.
2nd Narrator	The one who's getting married tomorrow.
Lee	But he called me stupid!
Kerry	I know he did. But he's only little.
Lee	That's not fair! He can say rude things to me. He can say what he likes to me, but I can't say anything back! Because he's little!

Lee stamps off, angrily. Kerry calls after him.

Kerry	Lee! Lee!

She turns back to Ross.

You shouldn't have called him stupid, Ross.

Ross   I don't care! He *is* stupid! And those trousers are
          stupid! They're too long and they'll trip me up
          and everyone will laugh at me! And I'm not
          wearing them!

          *Ross throws the trousers back onto the
          chair and stamps off angrily. Kerry
          calls after him.*

Kerry   Ross! Ross!

          She pauses.

          Oh, dear.

She picks up the trousers
and holds them up.

Kerry Ross is right. They are a bit long. But what can we do about it? It's too late to change them. The wedding's tomorrow.

She looks at the trousers as the
narrators *speak.*

1st Narrator So she looks at the trousers, and wonders what she can do.

2nd Narrator And suddenly, she gets an idea.

Kerry Got it! That's what I'll do!

She walks off with the trousers.

Scene 2

*The **narrators** remain on stage. **Ross** enters, still stamping angrily.*

1st Narrator   Meanwhile, Ross is still in a bad mood.

Ross   I'm not wearing them!

12

2nd Narrator	He's in a bad mood all day.
Ross	They can't make me!
1st Narrator	He stamps about the house.
Ross	I hate that frilly shirt.
2nd Narrator	He slams doors.
Ross	I hate that bow tie.
2nd Narrator	He scares the cat.
Ross	But most of all I hate those stupid trousers!

Lee enters.

Lee	You've only got to wear them for one day, Ross.
Ross	No, I haven't, because I'm not going to wear them at all.
Lee	Think about Kerry. You'll spoil her wedding day.
Ross	I don't care.

Lee   I think you'll look really smart in them.

Ross   No, I won't. I'll look stupid. They'll trip me up.
                       In a church! In front of all those people! I can just
                       hear what they'll say now!

*The two **narrators** act as people at the
church in Ross's imagination. They
point at him.*

2nd Narrator	Look at him!
1st Narrator	Look at those trousers!
2nd Narrator	Doesn't he look stupid!

They laugh.

Ross	Nobody's going to laugh at me. I'm not going to be a page boy!
Lee	What are you going to do, then?
Ross	I'm going to run away!
Lee	You can't do that!
Ross	Yes, I can. I hate those stupid trousers, and I hate you!

*Ross stamps off. Their **mum** enters
from the opposite side of stage and
speaks to Lee.*

Mum	Lee! Have you been upsetting your brother again!

Lee	No, Mum –
Mum	It sounds like it to me.
Lee	I haven't, really!
Mum	Why is he in such a bad mood, then? Why were the two of you shouting just now?
Lee	I wasn't shouting. *He* was –
Mum	It's not fair, you know, Lee. Your sister's getting married tomorrow, and I've got so many things to do. And all you can do is upset your little brother.
Lee	But I haven't – !
Mum	No more of it, Lee! Do you hear? Or you'll be in big trouble!

She goes.

Lee	My little brother! *He's* the one in the bad mood, and *I'm* the one who gets the blame! It's just not fair!

*Lee goes. The **narrators** speak.*

1st Narrator   And off he goes, in a bad mood –

2nd Narrator   Because his little brother's in a bad mood.

1st Narrator   Because he doesn't want to wear those stupid trousers.

2nd Narrator   But if they'd both stayed –

1st Narrator   If they'd stayed just a little bit longer –

2nd Narrator   They'd have seen that Kerry had solved the problem.

Kerry enters with the trousers. They are shorter now.

Kerry   There. A little bit cut off the bottom of the trousers, a needle and thread to sew them up again, and they're good as new.

She holds up the trousers.

Kerry   Just right. They'll fit him now.

She puts the trousers on the chair.

I'll leave them there for him. It'll be a nice
surprise when he finds them in the morning.

She goes.

Scene 3

*The **narrators** speak.*

1st Narrator   It looks like the problem's solved.

2nd Narrator   Kerry thinks the problem's solved.

1st Narrator   But Lee doesn't know the problem's solved.

2nd Narrator   And he lies awake in bed at night.

1st Narrator   He lies awake, thinking and worrying.

2nd Narrator   Worrying about his little brother.

1st Narrator	He likes him, really, and doesn't want him to run away.
2nd Narrator	But what can he do? How can he make his brother happy again?
1st Narrator	Suddenly, an idea pops into his head.
2nd Narrator	And in the middle of the night –
1st Narrator	In the dark, quiet house –
2nd Narrator	He creeps downstairs.

Lee comes creeping onstage in his pyjamas.

Lee   No one's heard me. They're all still asleep. And there are the trousers!

He goes to the chair and picks them up.

Now, all I need is a pair of scissors.

He goes off with the trousers.

1st Narrator   What's Lee doing now?

2nd Narrator   What's his idea, what's his plan?

1st Narrator   The house is quiet.

2nd Narrator   The house is dark.

1st Narrator   And the only sound that can be heard –

2nd Narrator   Is the snip, snip, snip of a pair of scissors.

Lee enters with the trousers. They're even shorter now.

Lee   There. I've cut a piece off the bottom of each leg.
             They should be short enough for him now.

He puts them on the chair.

             I'll leave them there. It'll be a nice surprise
             for him in the morning.

Lee goes.

1st Narrator   And off he goes, back to bed, and falls fast asleep.

2nd Narrator   But somebody else is still awake.

1st Narrator   Up in his bedroom, Ross can't sleep.

2nd Narrator	He doesn't want to run away.
1st Narrator	He doesn't know where he'd run to.
2nd Narrator	But he can't stand those stupid trousers.
1st Narrator	He doesn't want to wear them, but what can he do?
2nd Narrator	Suddenly, an idea pops into his head!

__Ross__ creeps onstage, in his pyjamas.

1st Narrator	He slips out of bed, he creeps downstairs.
2nd Narrator	It's spooky and dark. There are shadows on the walls.
1st Narrator	Big shadows all across the walls.
2nd Narrator	Like monsters with long fingers, reaching out to grab him.

*The two **narrators** pretend to be the shadows. They reach out towards Ross with their fingers and make a creepy sound.*

1st Narrator   Wooo!

2nd Narrator   Wooo!

**1st and
2nd Narrators**   WOOOOOO!

*Scared, **Ross** backs away from them and cries out.*

Ross	Aaaargh!

*The two **narrators** step back.*

1st Narrator	But there's no monster really.
2nd Narrator	He's just brushed up against the cat.
Ross	*(Bravely)* There's no such thing as monsters.
1st Narrator	And now he's in the living room.
2nd Narrator	And hanging on the chair are the trousers.

***Ross** picks up the trousers.*

Ross	I know just what to do. All I need is a pair of scissors.

He goes off with the trousers.

2nd Narrator	What's his idea, what's his plan?
1st Narrator	The house is quiet.
2nd Narrator	The house is dark.

1st Narrator	And the only sound that can be heard –
2nd Narrator	Is the snip, snip, snip of a pair of scissors.

Ross comes back with the trousers. They're even shorter now.

Ross	There. That's short enough. They won't trip me up now. And I won't have to run away.

He puts the trousers back on the chair and goes.

1st Narrator	And in the dark he creeps upstairs –
2nd Narrator	And gets back into bed and falls fast asleep.

Scene 4

*It's the next morning. **Mum** enters, humming softly to herself.*

1st Narrator   Next morning, their mum comes downstairs.

2nd Narrator   She's the first up. She's got a lot to do.

1st Narrator	It's her daughter's wedding day and she's very happy.
2nd Narrator	Until she sees the trousers on the chair.

Mum stops and looks at the trousers.

1st Narrator	She walks towards them.

Mum walks towards the trousers.

2nd Narrator	She picks them up.

She picks up the trousers.

1st Narrator	She looks at them.

Mum looks at the trousers.

2nd Narrator	She can't believe her eyes.
1st Narrator	And she screams!

Mum lets out a loud scream.

Mum	AAAARRRGH!

2nd Narrator	And everyone comes running!

Ross, Lee, and *Kerry* run onstage.

Kerry	What is it, Mum?
Lee	What's happened?
Kerry	What's wrong?
Mum	What's wrong? Look! Ross's trousers! Look at them!

Kerry takes the trousers off Mum and holds them up.

Kerry	What's happened to them? How did they get so short?
Lee	I don't know!
Ross	Don't ask me!
Kerry	I am asking you! I didn't do this, so it must have been one of you!

Lee	It wasn't me!
Ross	I didn't do that to them!
Kerry	Somebody did! Look at them! They're ruined!
Mum	All right, Kerry. Calm down. You don't want to get worked up on your wedding day.
Kerry	But look at them, Mum! They're not trousers any more. They're shorts!

Mum *takes the trousers from Kerry and holds them up.*

Mum   Perhaps he can still wear them, then. Try them on, Ross. They still might look all right.

Ross	No! No way! No way!
Kerry	Ross! Do as Mum says! Go and try them on!

Mum holds out the trousers to Ross. Sulkily, Ross takes them and goes off. Kerry speaks to Lee.

Kerry	Are you sure you don't know anything about this, Lee?
Lee	Well... I was worried about Ross... he said he was going to run away, and I didn't want him to. And I thought if the trousers were a bit shorter he'd wear them... so I came downstairs last night –
Mum	And shortened them?
Lee	Yes.
Kerry	But I'd already shortened them.
Lee	And I didn't shorten them that much! Perhaps it was Ross. Perhaps he came downstairs as well –

Mum   It doesn't matter. All they need is a bit of sewing round the bottom, and I'm sure he'll look all right in them.

Ross comes back on, wearing the red, frayed shorts. They all stare at him.

Mum   There, Ross. They don't look too bad.

Kerry   He looks quite sweet.

                 Ross is horrified.

Ross   I don't want to look sweet!

                 *Lee looks thoughtfully
                 at Ross. Mum is still
                 speaking to Ross.*

Mum	As I said, a bit of sewing round the bottom –
Lee	No! He can't wear them!
Kerry	Why not?
Lee	Look at his legs! They look really stupid! All white and skinny. They're horrible. Like two skinny white sticks!

Ross Stop saying –

Lee interrupts him.

Lee You really can't wear them with legs like that.
Can you, Ross?

*Ross suddenly realizes that Lee is
trying to help him.*

Ross No. Lee's right. My legs are horrible.

Lee He's got scabby knees. They'll make people sick.

Ross	He's right! I have! Look at them, Mum.
	They're so scabby they even make *me* sick!
Mum	Yes. I suppose Lee is right.
	Those trousers won't do at all.
	He'll have to wear something else.
Kerry	But what can he wear?
Lee	His own trousers.
	He's got those new grey ones
	Mum bought him for school. They're smart.
Ross	Yes! I'll wear those.
Kerry	All right. It looks like you'd better
	go and get those off – and throw them away.
Mum	And hurry up about it.
	We've all got to get ready for the wedding.

Mum and Kerry go off.
Ross turns to Lee.

Ross	Thank you, Lee. Thanks for being so rude to me. You saved me from having to wear these stupid trousers.
Lee	That's all right. Any time.
	*Ross and Lee go. The **narrators** speak.*
1st Narrator	So everything turns out well after all.
2nd Narrator	They all get dressed in their best and go off to the church.
1st Narrator	And Kerry gets married.
2nd Narrator	And everyone's happy.

Scene 5

*Outside the church. **Kerry** and **Mum** come onstage. **Kerry** is wearing a wedding-veil. The **1st Narrator** stands beside Kerry and takes her arm, acting as her husband. The **2nd Narrator** acts as a photographer.*

Mum

My little girl! All grown-up and married!

2nd Narrator

But they do look a lovely couple, don't they?

Mum	Yes. They do.
2nd Narrator	Are you ready for the photographs now?
Mum	Nearly. *(She calls out)* Lee! Ross! Come on! It's time for the photographs!
	*The **2nd Narrator** takes out a camera. **Lee** and **Ross** enter. **Ross** is wearing a pair of smart grey trousers.*
Mum	Come on, you two. Hurry up. Stand next to me.
2nd Narrator	Which one's the page-boy?
Ross	I am!
2nd Narrator	You look really smart. I'll take a photo of you on your own in a minute.
Ross	Great!

Ross and Lee stand by Mum
and they gather around Kerry
and her husband, as the
2nd Narrator prepares to take
a photograph.

Ross Thanks again, Lee.

Lee That's all right. What are brothers for?

Ross It's great day, isn't it?

Lee Yes. Especially when you get a thank you
from your little brother.
Just when you've been really rude to him.

Ross Yes. And all because of a pair of
stupid trousers.

They laugh.

2nd Narrator All right, everybody.
Stand still. Smile please!

*They all smile at the camera, and
freeze.*

THE END

Treetops Playscripts
Titles in the series include:

Stage 10
The Masked Cleaning Ladies of Om
by John Coldwell; adapted
by David Calcutt
single: 0 19 918780 0
pack of 6: 0 19 918781 9

Stupid Trousers
by Susan Gates; adapted by David Calcutt
single: 0 19 918782 7
pack of 6: 0 19 918783 5

Stage 11
Bertha's Secret Battle
by John Coldwell; adapted
by David Calcutt
single: 0 19 918786 X
pack of 6: 0 19 918787 8

Bertie Wiggins' Amazing Ears
by David Cox and Erica James; adapted
by David Calcutt
single: 0 19 918784 3
pack of 6: 0 19 918785 1

Stage 12
The Lie Detector
by Susan Gates; adapted by David Calcutt
single: 0 19 918788 6
pack of 6: 0 19 918789 4

Blue Shoes
by Angela Bull; adapted by David Calcutt
single: 0 19 918790 8
pack of 6: 0 19 918791 6

Stage 13
The Personality Potion
by Alan MacDonald; adapted
by David Calcutt
single: 0 19 918792 4
pack of 6: 0 19 918793 2

Spooky!
by Michaela Morgan; adapted
by David Calcutt
single: 0 19 918794 0
pack of 6: 0 19 918795 9

Stage 14
Petey
by Paul Shipton; adapted
by David Calcutt
single: 0 19 918796 7
pack of 6: 0 19 918797 5

Climbing in the Dark
adapted from his own novel
by Nick Warburton
single: 0 19 918798 3
pack of 6: 0 19 918799 1